W9-CAI-369

IH
#120

BEGINNING TO READ

A

HOUGHTON MIFFLIN LITERARY READERS

PROPERTY OF
MY SCHOOL DISTRICT OF MENU
MSIL #1

HOUGHTON MIFFLIN COMPANY   BOSTON

Atlanta   Dallas   Geneva, Illinois   Palo Alto   Princeton   Toronto

Program Authors

William K. Durr, John J. Pikulski, Rita M. Bean, J. David Cooper, Nicholas A. Glaser, M. Jean Greenlaw, Hugh Schoephoerster, Mary Lou Alsin, Kathryn Au, Rosalinda B. Barrera, Joseph E. Brzeinski, Ruth P. Bunyan, Jacqueline C. Comas, Frank X. Estrada, Robert L. Hillerich, Timothy G. Johnson, Pamela A. Mason, Joseph S. Renzulli

Senior Consultants

Jacqueline L. Chaparro, Alan N. Crawford, Alfredo Schifini, Sheila Valencia

Program Reviewers

Donna Bessant, Mara Bommarito, Yetive Bradley, Patricia M. Callan, Clara J. Hanline, Fannie Humphery, Barbara H. Jeffus, Beverly Jimenez, Sue Cramton Johnson, Michael P. Klentschy, Petra Montante, Nancy Rhodes, Julie Ryan, Lily Sarmiento, Ellis Vance, Judy Williams, Leslie M. Woldt, Janet Gong Yin

Acknowledgments

For each of the selections listed below, grateful acknowledgment is made for permission to adapt and/or reprint original or copyrighted material, as follows:

"Good-Night, Good Night," by Dennis Lee. From *Jelly Belly*, published by Blackie & Son Ltd. Copyright © 1982 by Dennis Lee. Reprinted by permission of the Colbert Agency Inc. for the author. Illustration from *Read-Aloud Rhymes for the Very Young*, edited by Jack Prelutsky. Text copyright © 1986 by Alfred A. Knopf, Inc. Illustrations © 1986 by Marc Brown. Used by permission of Alfred A. Knopf, Inc.

"Just Like Daddy," entire text and some art from the book by Frank Asch. Copyright © 1981 by Frank Asch. Used by permission of the publisher, Prentice Hall, Inc., Englewood Cliffs, New Jersey.

"Mary Wore Her Red Dress and Henry Wore His Green Sneakers," text and illustrations © 1985 by Merle Peek. Reprinted by permission of Clarion Books, a Houghton Mifflin company.

"Sleepy Bear," by Lydia Dabcovich. Copyright © 1982 by Lydia Dabcovich. Reprinted by permission of the publisher, E.P. Dutton, a division of NAL Penguin, Inc.

Credits

Illustrators: 4–5 Maxie Chambliss **6–20** Merle Peek **21–26** James Marshall **27–38** Lydia Dabcovich **39–46** David McPhail **47–61** Frank Asch **62** Marc Brown **63–71** James Marshall **72** Brinton Turkle

Copyright © 1989 by Houghton Mifflin Company.
All rights reserved.
No part of this work may be reproduced or transmitted in any form or by any means, electronic or mechanical, including photocopying and recording, or by any information storage or retrieval system without the prior written permission of the copyright owner, unless such copying is expressly permitted by federal copyright law. With the exception of non-profit transcription in Braille, Houghton Mifflin is not authorized to grant permission for further uses of copyrighted selections reprinted in this text without the permission of their owners. Permission must be obtained from the individual copyright owners as identified herein. Address requests for permission to make copies of Houghton Mifflin material to School Permissions, Houghton Mifflin Company, 222 Berkeley Street, Boston, MA 02116.

Printed in the U.S.A.
ISBN: 0-395-48009-4

OPQR-D-9987

Contents

Big Bears and Little Bears

Houghton Mifflin Literature
Deep in the Forest

3

A

Big Bears
and
Little Bears

5

Mary Wore Her Red Dress and Henry Wore His Green Sneakers

Written and Illustrated
by Merle Peek

Mary wore her red dress,
Red dress, red dress,
Mary wore her red dress
All day long.

Henry wore his green sneakers,
Green sneakers, green sneakers,

Henry wore his green sneakers
All day long.

Katy wore her yellow sweater,
Yellow sweater, yellow sweater,

10

Katy wore her yellow sweater
All day long.

Ben wore his blue jeans,
   Blue jeans, blue jeans,
Ben wore his blue jeans
   All day long.

Amanda wore her brown bandana,
Brown bandana, brown bandana,
Amanda wore her brown bandana
All day long.

Ryan wore his purple pants,
Purple pants, purple pants,

Ryan wore his purple pants
All day long.

Stacy wore her violet ribbons,
Violet ribbons, violet ribbons,

Stacy wore her violet ribbons
All day long.

Kenny wore his orange shirt,
Orange shirt, orange shirt,
Kenny wore his orange shirt
All day long.

Who wore a pink hat,
Pink hat, pink hat,
Who wore a pink hat
All day long?

Katy wore a pink hat,
Pink hat, pink hat,
Katy wore a pink hat
All night long.

The Boat

Written and Illustrated by
James Marshall

22

24

Sleepy Bear

Written and Illustrated by
Lydia Dabcovich

It's getting cold.

Leaves are falling.

Birds are leaving

and bear is sleepy.

He finds a cave.

It snows and snows.

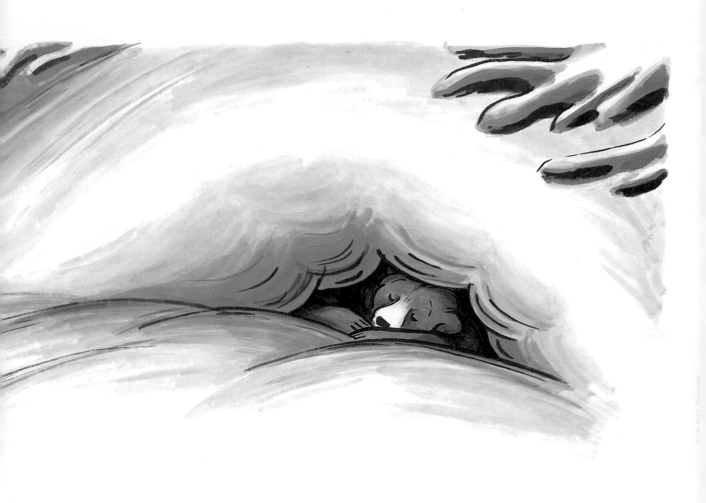

But bear is cozy
in his cave.

The sun comes out again.
Birds come back.

Bugs come back.

Bees come back.

Bear remembers honey.
He follows the bees.

Come In, Boo Bear

Written and Illustrated by David McPhail

Boo Bear and Mother went
to the beach.

"Come in, Boo!" said Pig.
"It's fun!"

"I don't want to," said Boo.
"I won't like it."

"It's fun in the water," said Mother.
"You will like it."

"I won't like it," Boo said.

"I want to go in," said Mother.
"I want to have fun."

"You go in," said Boo.
"I have to think."

"Come in, Boo," said Mother and Pig.

"OK, I'll do it," said Boo.

"Will you help?"

Pig said, "We will help you, Boo. You will like the water."

Boo went in the water.

"Here we go," said Mother.

"I don't think I like it," said Boo.
"I think I want to go home."

Pig said, "Boo! You will have fun."

"I did it!" said Boo.

"You did!" said Pig.
"What do you think?
Do you like the water?"

Boo said, "I think I do.
I think the water is fun!"

"Come out, Boo," said Mother Bear.
"We have to go home."

"Do we have to go <u>now</u>?" said Boo.

Mother said, "Yes, we do."

"I don't want to go home," said Boo.
"I think I like it in here."

"Boo," said Mother.
"You didn't want to go in.
Now you don't want to come out.
What a bear!"

What a bear!

Just Like Daddy

Written and Illustrated by
Frank Asch

When I got up this morning
I yawned a big yawn . . .
Just like Daddy.

I washed my face, got dressed,
and had a big breakfast . . .
Just like Daddy.

51

Then I put on my coat
and my boots . . .
Just like Daddy.

And we all went fishing.

On the way I picked a flower
and gave it to my mother . . .
Just like Daddy.

When we got to the lake,
I put a big worm on my hook . . .
Just like Daddy.

All day we fished and fished,
and I caught a big fish . . .
Just like Mommy!

Good Night, Good Night

By Dennis Lee

The dark is dreaming.
Day is done.
Good night, good night
To everyone.

Good night to the birds,
And the fish in the sea,
Goodnight to the bears
And good night to me.

The Hat

Written and Illustrated by
James Marshall

Cat went to The Hat Shop.

"Hello, Cat," said Dog.
"Have you come to get a hat?"

"Yes, Dog. I need a hat," said Cat.
"I think I can help you," said Dog.
"Come in. Come in."

"Now here is a good hat," said Dog.
"Do you like it?"

"It's a good hat," said Cat.
"But I think it's too big."

"Too big?" said Dog.
"I don't think it's too big.
Put it on."

65

Cat put on the hat.

"I can't see," he said.

"But you look good!" said Dog.

"I do?" said Cat.

"You do, Cat, you do.
You look good," said Dog.

"Then I'll take it!" said Cat.

Cat went out.
He didn't see Bear and Rabbit.

"I think I see Cat," said Bear.

"Hello, Cat. Is it you?" said Rabbit.

"Yes, it is I," said Cat.

"Do you like my hat?"

"It's a good hat," said Rabbit.
"But don't you think it's too big?"

"I do not!" said Cat.

"Yes, Cat, it's too big," said Bear.

"It is not too big!" said Cat.
"I will now go home!"

"Look out, Cat!" said Bear.

"Help! Help!" said Cat.

Rabbit said, "Here we come, Cat.
We will help you."

"Poor Cat!" said Bear.
"You can't see!"

"Help! I need help!" said Cat.

"Poor Cat!" said Rabbit.
"Help is here.
We will take you home."

"My poor hat!" said Cat.

"Now, Cat," said Bear.
"Don't you think the hat is too big?"

"OK," said Cat. "The hat is too big.
But it did look good!"

Deep in the Forest
by BRINTON TURKLE

≈ *Houghton Mifflin Literature* ≈

You have read about big bears and little bears. This is a bear story for you to tell.

Who lives in a little house deep in the forest? You will be surprised!